the
Brooklyn Tabernacle Choir

LIVE
...again

Produced by Lari Goss
Choral arrangements by Don Hart and Carol Cymbala
Transcribed by Danny Zaloudik and Bill Wolaver

COMPANION MATERIALS

Choir Book	3010178018
Listening Cassette	7019098509
Listening Compact Disc	7019098606
"TRAX" Accompaniment Cassette	3014156086
Studio Orchestration	3010247257

The Studio Orchestrations are available individually. For more information contact: Music Department   •   The Brooklyn Tabernacle   •   290 Flatbush Avenue   •   Brooklyn, NY 11217   •   Phone # (718) 783-0942.

WORD MUSIC

Printed by Davis Brothers Publishing Co., Inc., Waco, TX

CONTENTS

Give God the Glory

Words and Music by
J. HILL

Choral Arr. by Don Hart

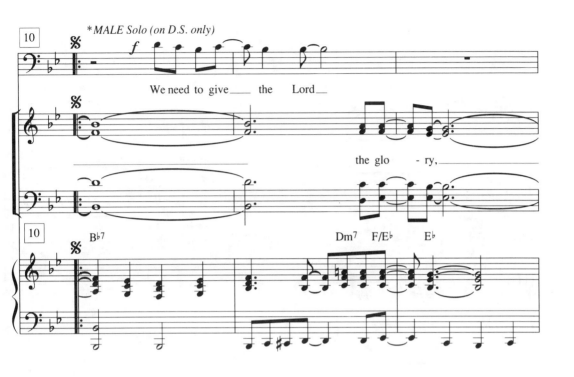

Optional alto solo.

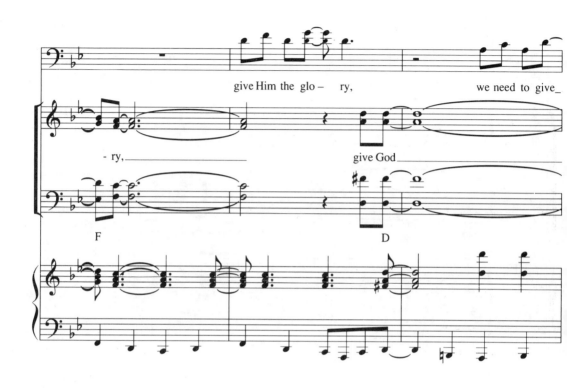

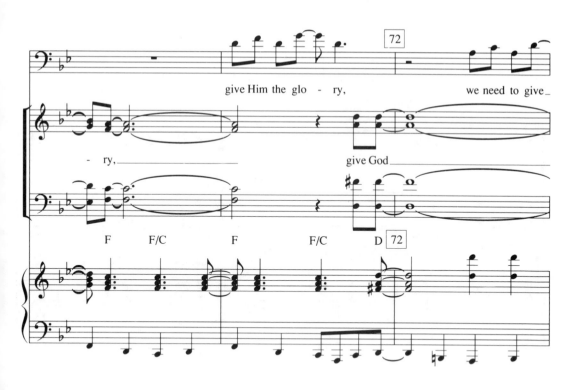

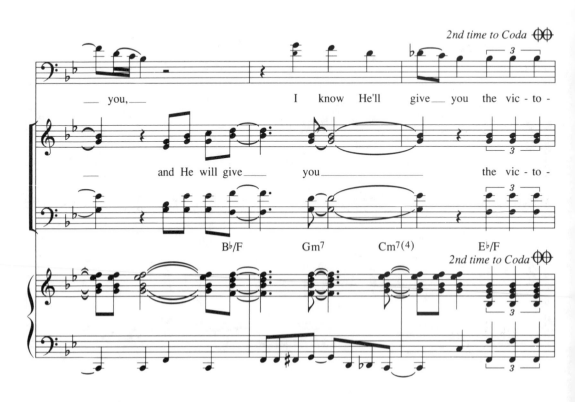

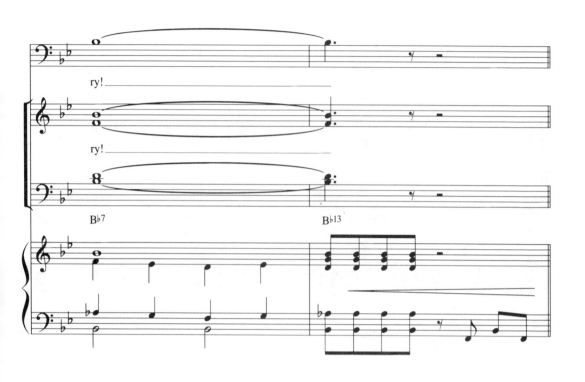

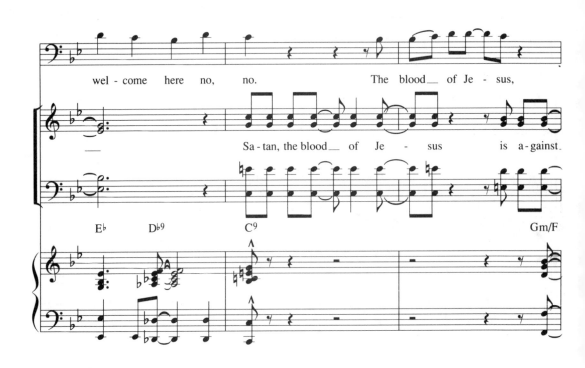

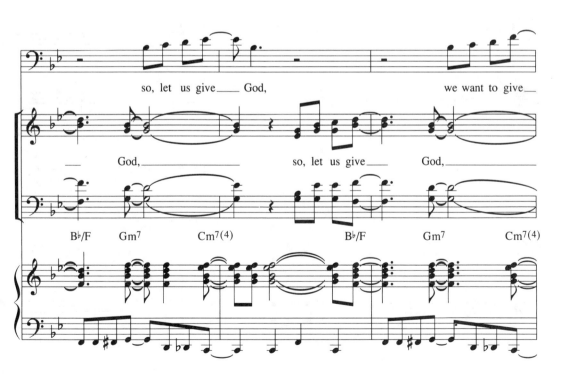

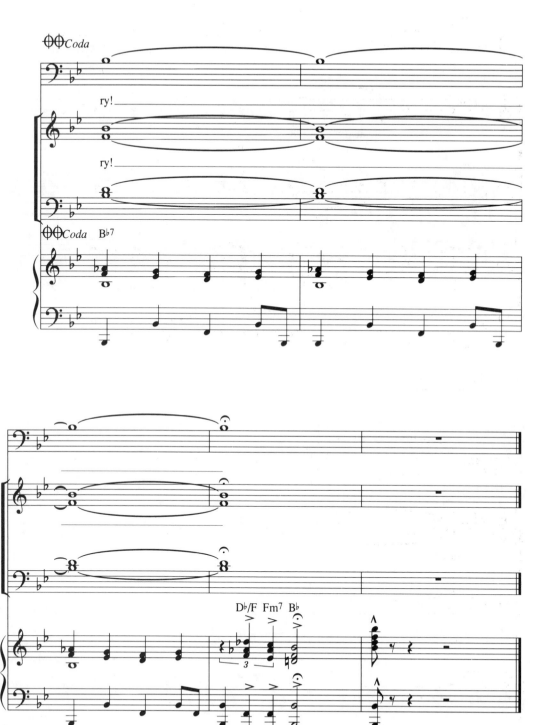

Right Now is the Right Time

Words and Music by
BABBIE MASON

Choral Arr. by Don Hart

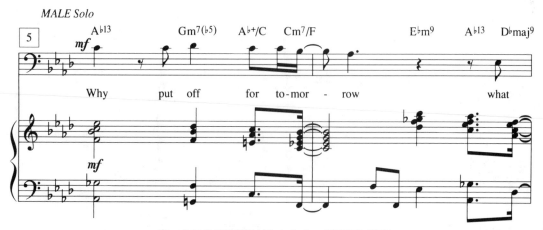

Right now is the right____ time____ to re-

Right now is the right____ time.____

G♭/B♭　A♭/C　G♭/D♭　D♭　Fm7/C

joice in what the Lord has done.____ There's

Ooo____

A♭maj9/B♭　B♭13(♭5)　D♭/E♭　E♭m7

mf

no bet - ter time___ than the pres - ent for

unis. **mf**
No bet - ter time___ than the

unis.

Fm7   Ebm7   Gbmaj7/Ab   Ab9

mf

rais - ing a song___ towards heav - en right_____ now.

pres - ent   rais - ing a song___ right now.

Dbmaj9   Gb9   Ab/Eb

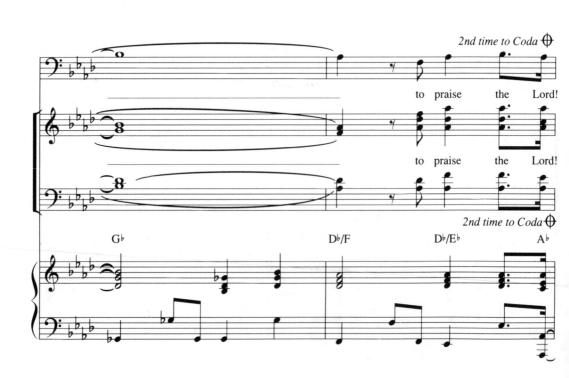

Now, we look

for - ward to the fu - ture but to -

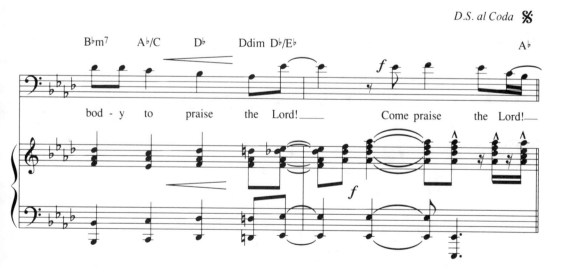

29

Now, He has

giv - en us___ this mo - ment, we'll nev - er

pass   this   way____   a - gain._____

This   is   the   day____   the   Lord____   has   made,_____

let us re - joice____ and be glad.

let us re - joice____ and be glad,   right now!

B♭sus   D/E   A

65

Right   now   is   the right____   time   to   praise   the   Lord!

Right   now   is   the right____   time   to   praise   the   Lord!

65   A   Bm   A/C♯   G/D   D   D/E   A

cued notes 2nd time only

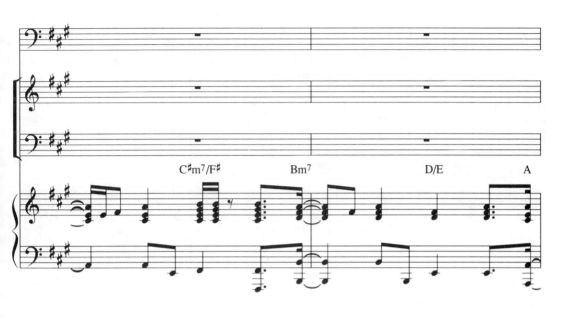

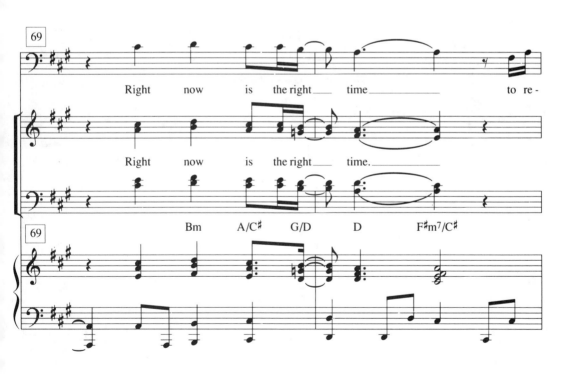

34

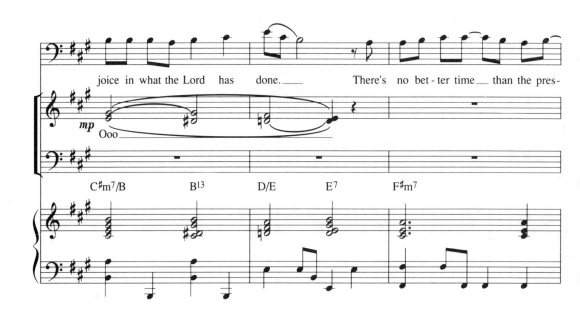

name

right now.___

Right now is the right___ time.

Bm   A/C#   G/D   D   D/E   A

___

Ah, right

Right now is the right___ time.

Bm   A/C#   G/D   D   D/E   A

He's Been Faithful

Words and Music by
CAROL CYMBALA
Choral Arr. by Don Hart

* or a few voices

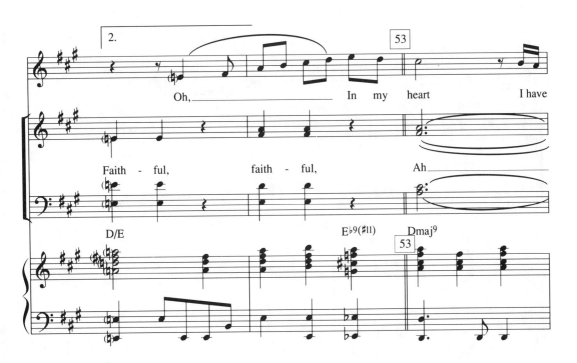

ques - tioned, e - ven failed to be - lieve yet, He's been

Ah

G#m7   C#7(b9)   F#m9   F#m7   C#m7/F#   F#7(b9)

faith - ful, faith - ful. In my heart I have

faith - ful, faith - ful. Ah

A/B   A+/B   D/E   Eb9(#11)   Dmaj7

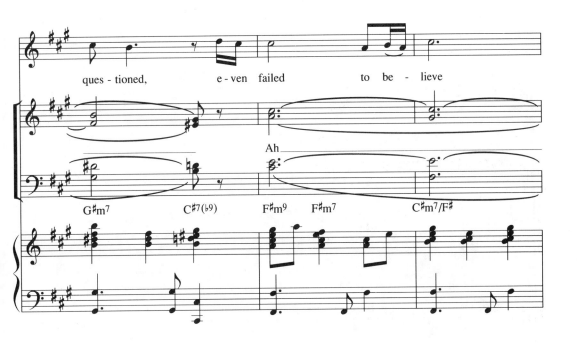

ques-tioned, e-ven failed to be-lieve

Ah

G#m7   C#7(b9)   F#m9   F#m7   C#m7/F#

yet, He's been faith-ful, faith-ful to

to

faith-ful, faith-ful

to

F#13(b9)   F#7+5   A/B   A+/B   D/E

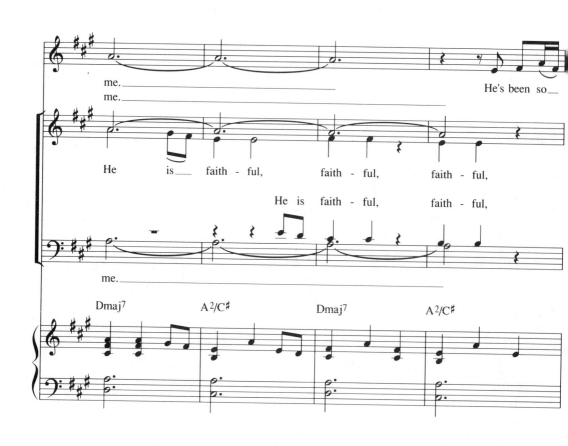

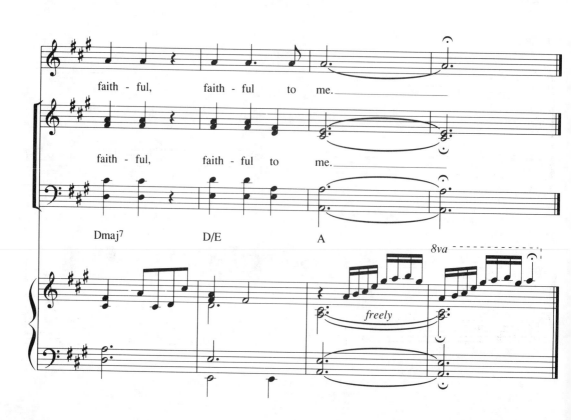

Great Is Thy Faithfulness

THOMAS O. CHISHOLM

WILLIAM M. RUNYAN
Choral Arr. by Don Hart

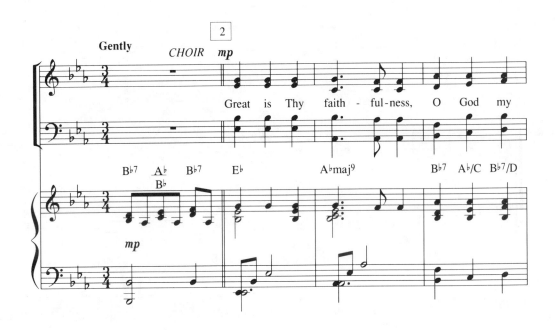

Revival in the Land

Words and Music by
RENEE MORRIS

Choral Arr. by Don Hart

60

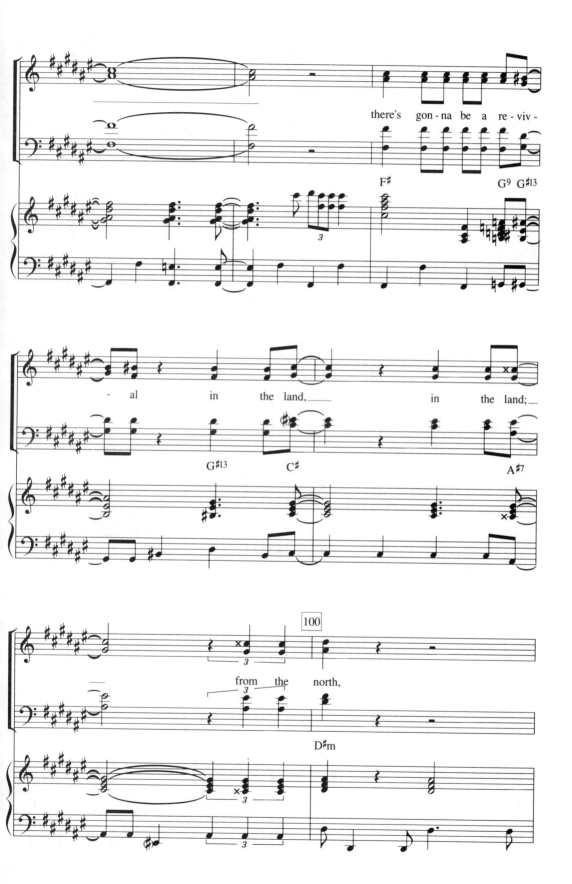

64

Daystar
(Shine Down on Me)

Words and Music by
STEVE RICHARDSON

Choral Arr. by Don Hart

door._____

door._____

A♭   A♭9   A9

Let me know__ Your wis - dom,   show me things__ I've nev - er seen be-

Let me know__ Your wis - dom,   show me things__ I've nev - er seen be-

B♭9   B♭7   B♭13   B♭9

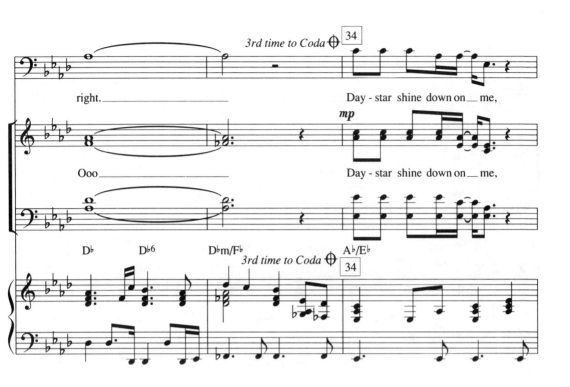

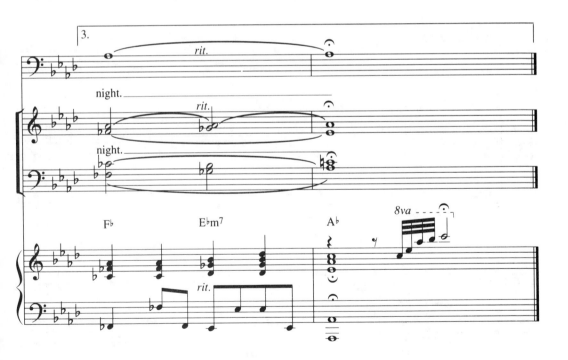

Grace Greater Than Our Sin

JULIA H. JOHNSTON

DANIEL B. TOWNER
Arranged by Carol Cymbala
Choral Arr. by Don Hart

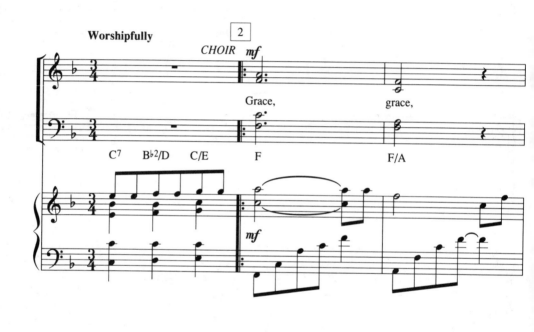

I Bowed On My Knees
and Cried Holy

Composer Unknown

Arranged by Lari Goss
Choral Arr. by Don Hart

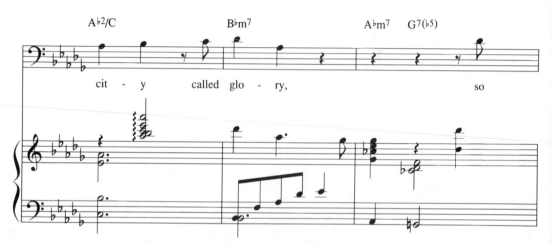

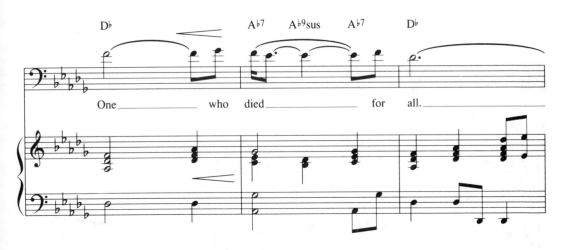

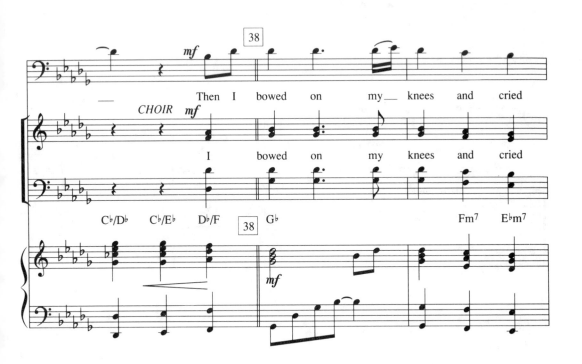

God._____ Glo - ry to the

God._____ Glo - ry to the

D♭ E♭m7 D♭/F G♭ D♭/A♭

Son____ of God._____ Then as I

Son____ of God._____

A♭ B♭m7 A♭7/C D♭ D♭2 A A7

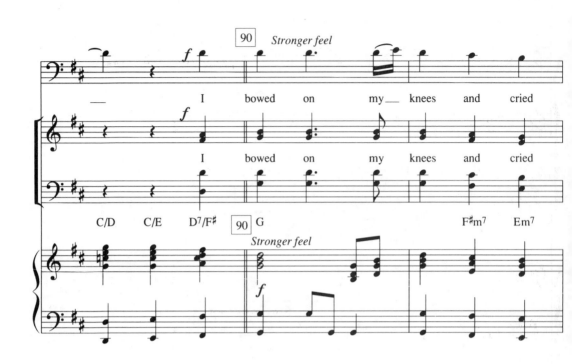

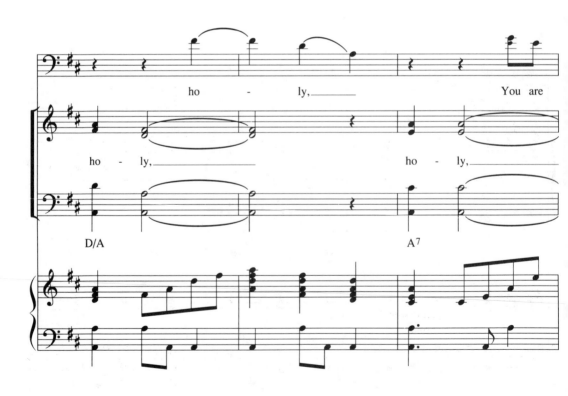

ho - ly, my God is ho - ly._ I

_ ho - ly._ I

G/D   D   Em⁷   D⁷/F♯

clapped   my   hands   and   sang   glo - ry,_

clapped   my   hands   and   sang   glo - ry,_

98   G   F♯m⁷   Em⁷   D/A

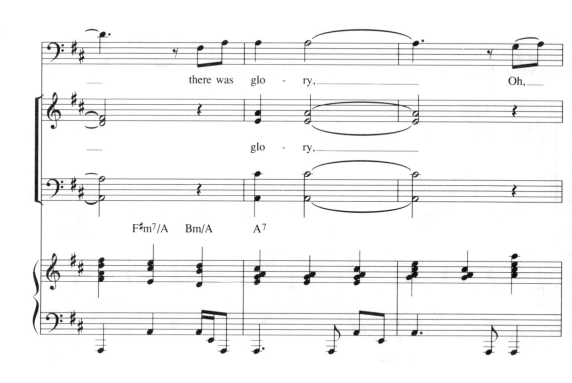

Father, I Adore You

Words and Music by
TERRYE COELHO
Choral Arr. by Don Hart

Thanks

Words and Music by
CARROLL McGRUDER

Choral Arr. by Don Hart

With energy ♩ = 80

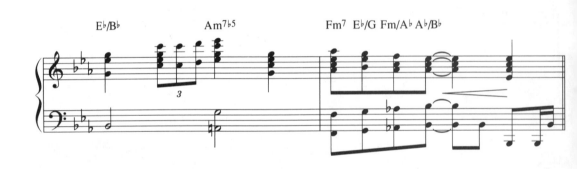

Thanks, thanks, I give You thanks___ for

done._____ I am so blessed, my

done._____

soul is at rest, O Lord,___ I give You thanks. _

2nd time to Coda

MALE Solo *mf*

E-ven in the bad times,

One Less Stone

**Words and Music by
DAVID HUFF**
Choral Arr. by Don Hart

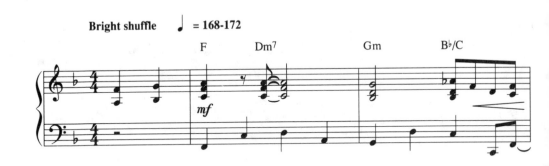

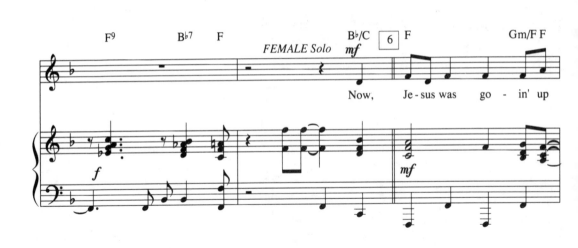

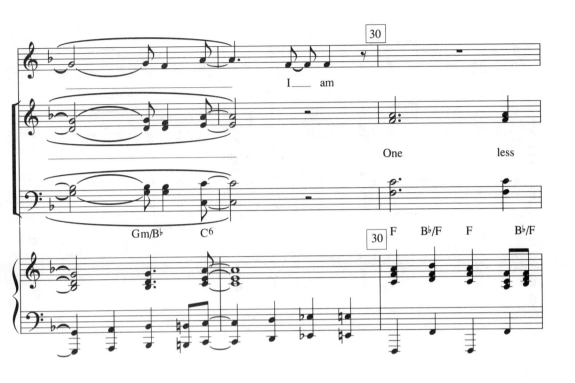

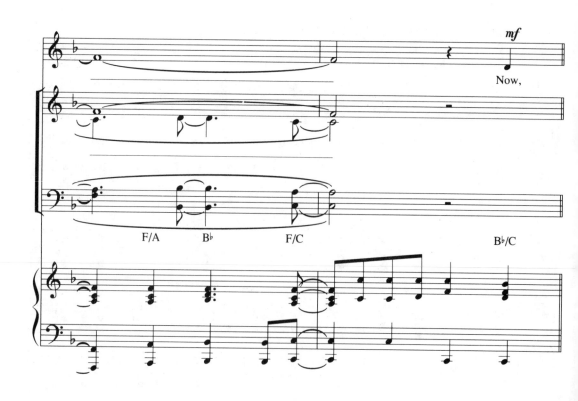

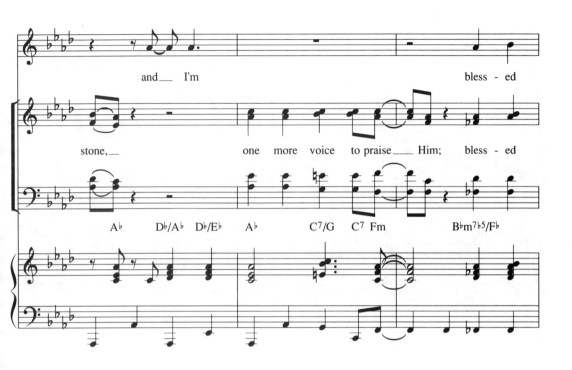

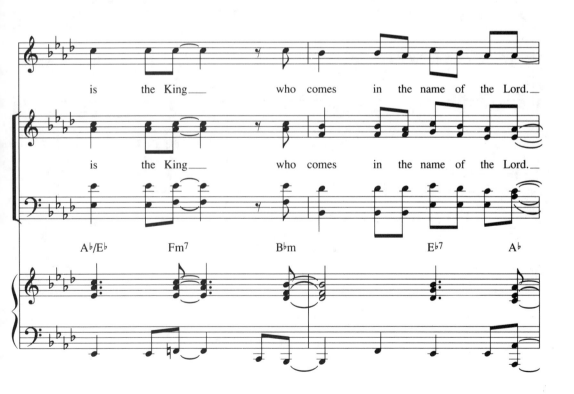

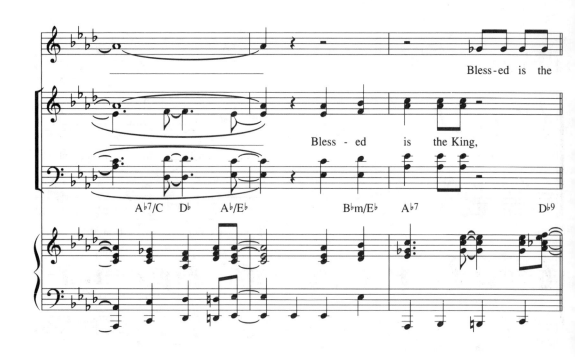

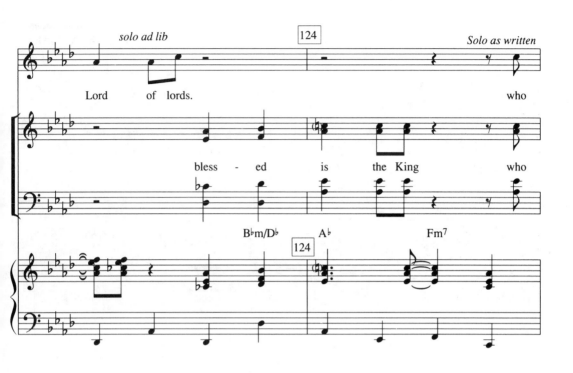

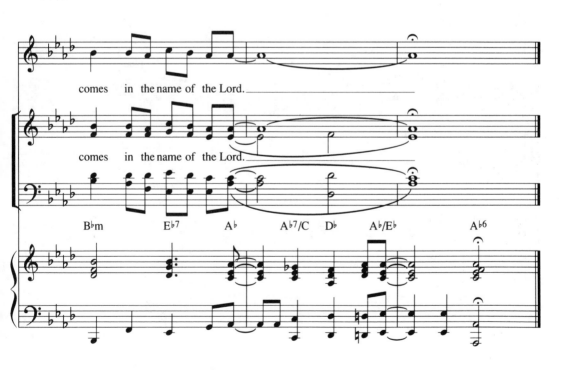

All I Want Is You, Lord

**Words and Music by
CAROL CYMBALA**
Choral Arr. by Don Hart

*or a few voices.

You_____ Lord, all_____ I

You_____ Lord, all_____ I

Cmaj7 Cmaj9 Am7 C/D

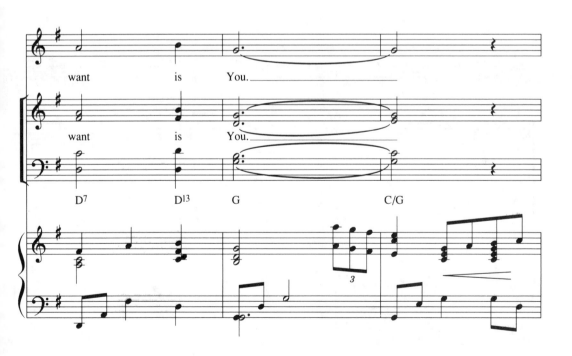

want is You._____

want is You._____

D7 D13 G C/G

Friend of a Wounded Heart

CLAIRE CLONINGER

WAYNE WATSON
Choral Arr. by Don Hart

* *or a few voices.*

Je - sus,___ the friend of a wound - ed heart.___

G/F   F   C/F   Dm⁷/G   C²

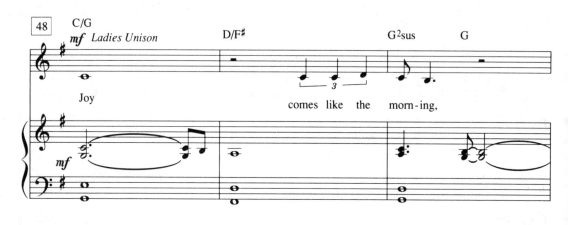

48 C/G
mf *Ladies Unison*   D/F♯   G²sus   G

Joy   comes like the morn - ing,

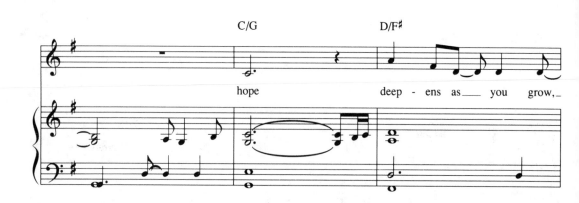

C/G   D/F♯

hope   deep - ens as___ you   grow,___

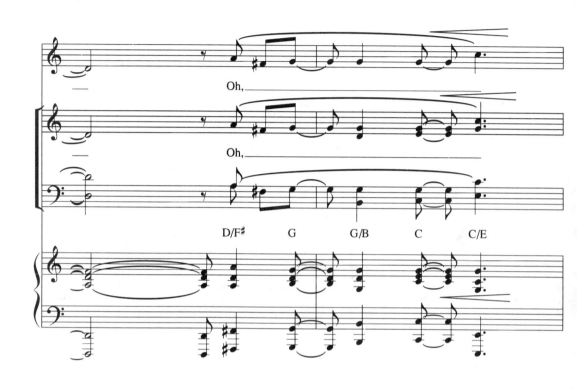

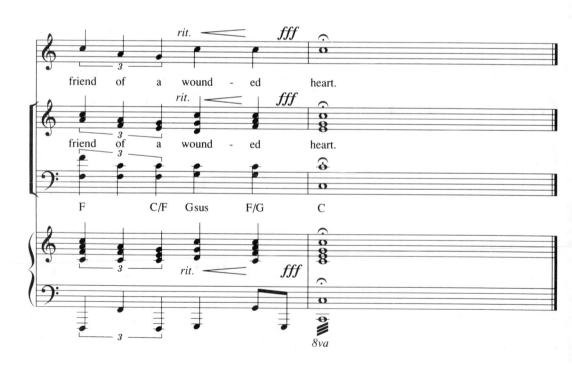

Jesus, Rock of Ages

**Words and Music by
CAROL CYMBALA**
Choral Arr. by Don Hart

We Will Overcome

Words and Music by
CAROL CYMBALA
Choral Arr. by Don Hart

Je - sus Christ, __ the con - quer - or, the ev - er great "I

D♭maj7   A♭2/C   D♭maj7   Dm7♭5

rit.   **23** *Faster* ♩ = 72

AM!"

CHOIR: unison **mf** *rit.*

We will o - ver-come through the blood of the

D♭/E♭   E♭7♭9   A♭2   A♭   A♭maj7   D♭/A♭

23 *Faster* ♩ = 72

rit.

mf

Lamb._____ We will o - ver-come

Ab2   Ab   Gm7b5   C7b9   Fm7

mf

Thru His

through the blood of the Lamb._____

Ab/Bb   Bb7   Bbm7   Db/Eb   D9(#11)

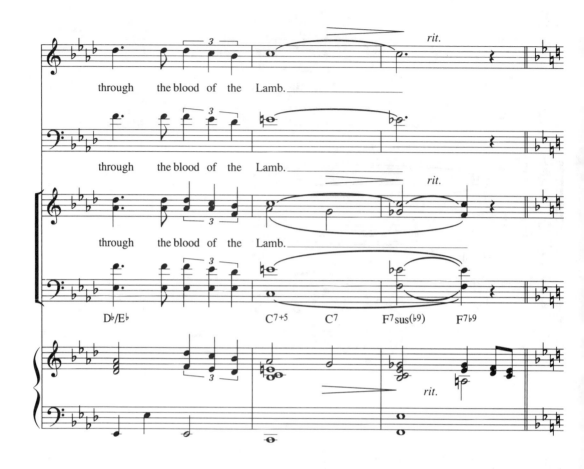

through the blood of the Lamb.

through the blood of the Lamb.

through the blood of the Lamb.

through the blood of the Lamb.

Db/Eb   C7+5   C7   F7sus(b9)   F7b9

39 * "My Faith Looks Up To Thee"

Slower

(solo-or opt. tenors unison)

My   faith   looks   up   to Thee,   Thou   Lamb   of

Bb2   F7/C   Dm7   Bb/D   Am7b5

Slower

* TEXT: Ray Palmer
  MUSIC: Lowell Mason

*"Holy, Holy, Holy"

rall.

53 rubato

whol - ly thine.

whol - ly thine.

Ho - ly, ho - ly,

G♭m6/A   A♭2sus A♭   C♭/D♭   Ḋ♭7   G♭   E♭m7

mp   rubato

* TEXT: Reginald Heber
MUSIC: John B. Dykes

D♭/F   G♭2   C♭maj7   D♭2/C♭   B♭m7

ho - ly!   Lord   God   Al - might - y!

D♭/F   G♭   D♭/F   E♭m   A♭7/E♭   D♭2/F   D♭/F G♭   D♭/A♭   G♭/A♭   A♭7

Ear - ly in the morn - ing our song shall rise to

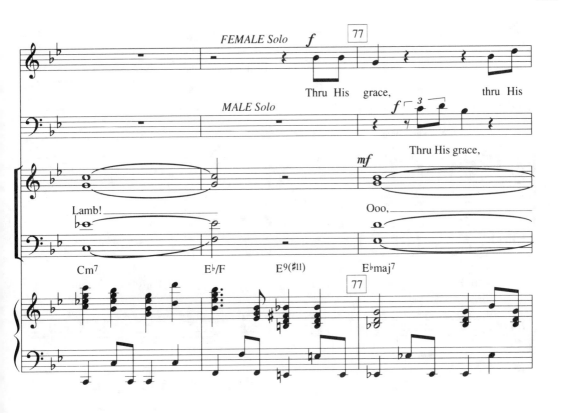

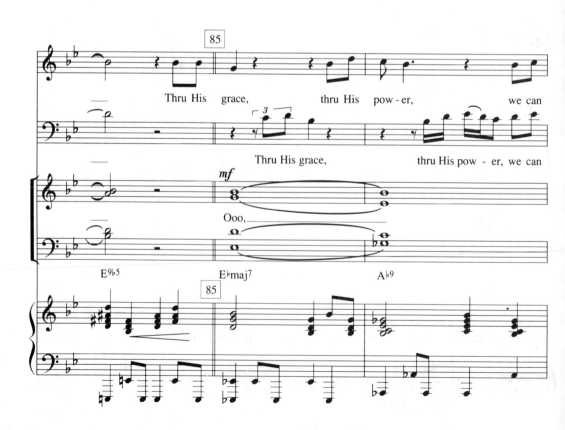

163

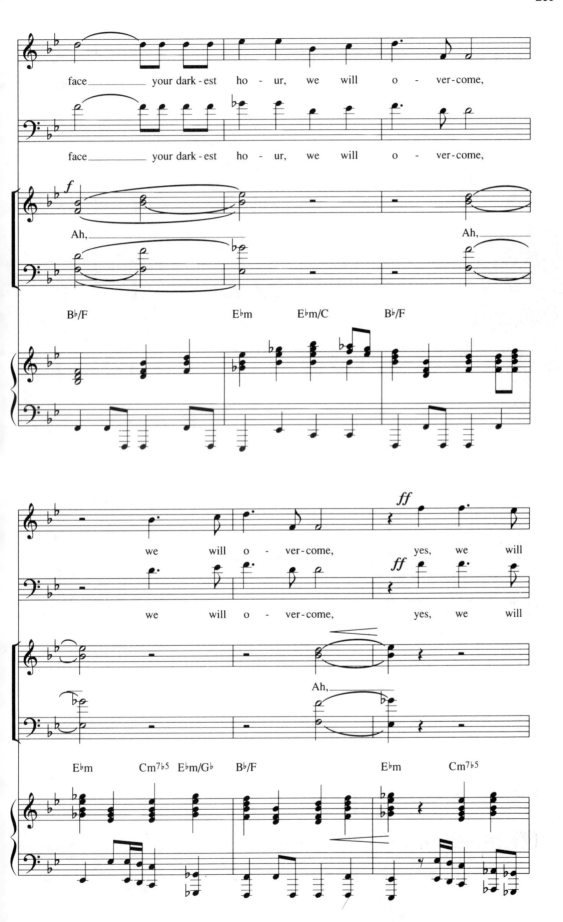

Fairer Than the Lilies
(He Is Fairer)
CLOSING

Anonymous
Choral Arr. by Don Hart